By Mary Man-Kong
Illustrated by Elisa Marrucchi

First published by Parragon in 2012
Parragon
Queen Street House
4 Queen Street
Bath BA1 1HE, UK
www.parragon.com

ISBN 978-1-4454-4748-3

Printed in China

Teachers' Pet

A little story for little learners

Bath • New York • Singapore • Hong Kong • Cologne • Delhi
Melbourne • Amsterdam • Johannesburg • Auckland • Shenzhen

Chip learns to read.
Belle is his teacher.
She teaches Chip
the alphabet.

A is for apple.

B is for books.

C is for Chip!

Now Chip reads
to Belle.
He has fun!

Some fish take
a music class
with Ariel.

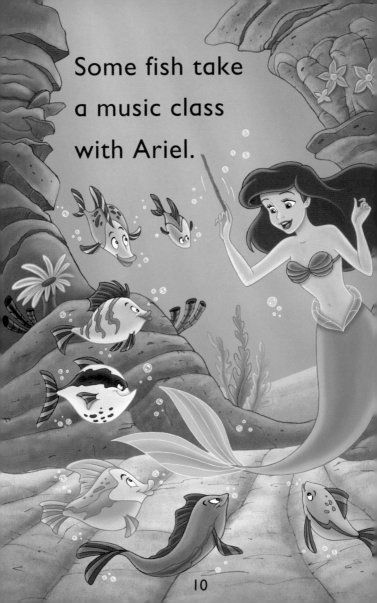

The fish play
the coral tubes.
They strum the
seaweed.

The fish blow
into pretty shells.
Sebastian and Flounder
dance to the music.

Ariel sings while her class plays. They all make beautiful music.

Tiana teaches kids
to make gumbo.
Tiana adds a pinch
of salt.

She adds a dash
of pepper.
Then a student
stirs the pot.

Tiana and her students taste the gumbo. It is yummy.

16

They share it
with their friends.

Cinderella teaches
Gus and Jaq to dance.

One, two, three.
One, two, three.

Gus and Jaq go
to a mouse ball.
They dance
the night away.

Cinderella is
very proud!

Rajah loves
to play games.
Jasmine teaches Rajah
to play hide-and-seek.

Rajah hides
behind a table.
Jasmine finds Rajah.

Now Jasmine hides
in a basket.

Rajah finds Jasmine.

Hide-and-seek is fun!

Aurora teaches
Buttercup tricks.
He jumps hurdles.

He trots in a circle.
The good fairies cheer!

Buttercup wins
the Royal Riding Contest!
He gets a ribbon.
He takes a bow.

29